Beginners Harmonica

Do you know a few of these traditional songs or tunes?

If so, then you can easily learn to play them on the harmonica by following the simple instructions in this book

An optional cassette recording (DMPMC9602) is available from the publishers
- *play along with it or use it to familiarise yourself with the tunes*

Beginners Harmonica, first produced and published in England 1996 by
Dave Mallinson Publications, 3 East View, Moorside, Cleckheaton, West Yorkshire, England BD19 6LD
Telephone: 01274 876388, facsimile: 01274 865208, e-mail: mally@jorum.demon.co.uk
ISBN 1 899512 42 X: a catalogue in print record for this title is available from the British Library
Devised by Steve Jennings; data input by Dave Mallinson and David J Taylor; drawings by Bruce M Baillie
Cover design by Bryan Ledgard, Ledgard Jepson Ltd, telephone 01226 766608
Cover photographs, data manipulation and typesetting by David J Taylor
Printed in England by RAP Ltd, Rochdale, telephone 01706 44981
All rights reserved
Text set in Garamond; music engraved in Petrucci
All tunes traditional, arranged Steve Jennings 1996

Rudiments of music

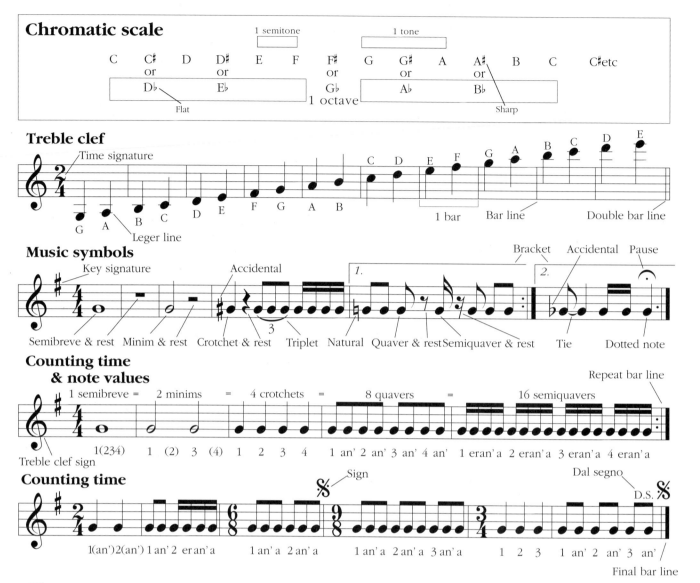

Chromatic scale

1 semitone · 1 tone

C · C♯ or D♭ · D · D♯ or E♭ · E · F · F♯ or G♭ · G · G♯ or A♭ · A · A♯ or B♭ · B · C · C♯etc

Flat · 1 octave · Sharp

Treble clef

Time signature · C D E F G A B C D E · 1 bar · Bar line · Double bar line

G A B C D E F G A B · Leger line

Music symbols

Key signature · Accidental · Bracket · Accidental · Pause · 1. · 2.

Semibreve & rest · Minim & rest · Crotchet & rest · Triplet · Natural · Quaver & rest · Semiquaver & rest · Tie · Dotted note

Counting time & note values

1 semibreve = · 2 minims = · 4 crotchets = · 8 quavers = · 16 semiquavers · Repeat bar line

Treble clef sign · 1(234) · 1 (2) 3 (4) · 1 2 3 4 · 1 an' 2 an' 3 an' 4 an' · 1 eran'a 2 eran'a 3 eran'a 4 eran'a

Counting time

Sign · Dal segno · D.S.

2/4 · 6/8 · 9/8 · 3/4

1(an')2(an') 1 an' 2 er an'a · 1 an'a 2 an'a · 1 an'a 2 an'a 3 an'a · 1 2 3 1 an' 2 an' 3 an'

Final bar line

Glossary

Chromatic scale — consists entirely of semitones.

Diatonic scale — consists of a series of notes from the chromatic scale at set intervals, e.g. the major scale (do-re-me etc) has intervals of: *tone, tone, semitone, tone tone, tone, semitone*. Thus the scale of C is *C, D, E, F, G, A, B, C* and the scale of D is *D, E, F♯, G, A, B C♯, D*. Tunes take all or most of their notes from a particular diatonic scale. Each scale has its own set number of sharps or flats.

Key signature — shows which notes have to be sharpened or flattened. It also gives an indication of the key. Keys are named by the first note of the scale.

Accidental — is a note which is altered to *sharp, flat* or *natural* and is foreign to the key indicated by the key signature. An accidental sign applies to the note it precedes and - unless contradicted - all further notes of that pitch up to the end of the bar.

Time signature — resembles a fraction. The top number indicates the number of beats per bar; the bottom number indicates the time unit for the beat (2 = a minim, 4 = a crotchet, 8 = a quaver, 16 = a semiquaver). For example, 4/4 = 4 beats per bar occurring every crotchet.

Rest — denotes a period of silence, of specified length.

Triplet — consists of three notes played in the time of two of the same value.

Tie — joins two notes of the same pitch; it denotes a single sustained note with a time value of the two combined.

Dotted note — a dot placed after a note lengthens that note by half. Thus

Double bar line — marks the end of an individual section or part. A 'final' bar line indicates the end of a piece or of a principal section. A final bar line preceded by two dots indicates that that particular section has to be repeated.

Bracket — play the bar under '1' the first time through; substitute the bar under '2' on the repeat.

Dal segno — return to the sign and repeat.

Fine — (pronounced 'feenay') means end.

Chord formations

Chord	B♭	F	C	G	D	A	E	B	F♯	Gm	Dm	Am	Em	Bm	F♯m	C7	G7	D7	A7	E7	B7
Root	B♭	F	C	G	D	A	E	B	F♯	G	D	A	E	B	F♯	C	G	D	A	E	B
Third	D	A	E	B	F♯	C♯	G♯	D♯	A♯	B♭	F	C	G	D	A	E	B	F♯	C♯	G♯	D♯
Fifth	F	C	G	D	A	E	B	F♯	C♯	D	A	E	B	F♯	C♯	G	D	A	E	B	F♯
Seventh																B♭	F	C	G	D	A

About the harmonica

IRST THINGS FIRST: the tunes in this book are written in both standard music notation and special *harmonica tablature,* to be played on a 'blues harp' in the key of D. Don't worry if your harmonica doesn't actually say on it 'Blues Harp'; it doesn't matter (similar instruments have names 'Marine Band', 'Special 20', 'Pro Harp', 'Cross Harp', 'Lee Oskar', 'Folk Blues', 'Big River' and 'Folkmaster' to name but a few) as long as it is single reeded with 10 holes. It doesn't even matter if you have a harmonica in another key, just pretend it is in D and play the hole numbered as shown in the tablature - the pitches of the notes will alter but their relationship to each other will remain the same.

The tremolo-tuned harmonica has long been popular among players of traditional music, because each note is produced by the simultaneous action of two reeds which produces a particular sound well suited to traditional music. The downside of this is that their notes are not so readily susceptible to the advanced techniques mentioned below. Sadly, tremolo instruments are now very hard to come by in keys other than C and G. For practical purposes, such an instrument pitched in D can be played in both D major and E minor.

This is OK if you are playing by yourself but if you are playing with other musicians they will need to transpose their accompaniment to match the key of your instrument - see page 22.

Musical notes have 'pitch' - this is how low (as in the left hand notes of a piano) or how high (like the right hand notes of the piano) that a particular sound happens to be. Harmonicas, like many instruments such as recorder, saxophone etc., are available in many different pitches. What this means is that the *same* holes on *different* pitch instruments will give you higher or lower notes.

A piece of music can also have a 'pitch' called the *key.* There are twelve possible keys, one for each note of music; each of these keys can either be major or minor. Major and minor keys produce different effects, or moods. Generally, music in a major key will sound 'happier' than music in a minor key.

The keys in which a harmonica can be played will depend upon its type. The common single-reeded Richter-tuned, (see separate box for explanation) major diatonic harmonica often known as a 'blues harp' is theoretically playable in all keys. This is the most widely-used instrument by far these days. For practical purposes most players using such an instrument pitched in D stick to the keys of D major, A major and E minor and more occasionally B minor, F♯ minor and rarely G major and C major. Playing all these keys apart from D major and E minor requires the player to have a good command of the techniques known as *bending, blow-bending, overblowing* and *overdrawing,* which allow the playing of notes that are not 'built-in' to the instrument. You will not need to use any of these advanced techniques for any of the tunes in this book, though you well may wish to go on and study them later, as you become a more confident and imaginative player.

Layout of a blues harp in D

HERE IS A diagram showing all the notes available, 'built-in' on the 10 hole Richter-tuned major diatonic harmonica in the key of D, for which the tunes in this book have been arranged. The notes that are available by blowing are shown in capital letters and those obtained by drawing are shown in lower case.

Note layout on a harmonica in D:

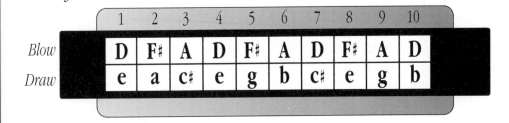

The tablature

HERE IS ANOTHER representation of the information contained in the layout diagram, this time as musical notation and harmonica tablature. The tablature is easy to understand. A plain number means blow that hole; a number in a circle means draw (suck). The names of the notes are given below the tablature.

Notes available on a harmonica in D:

Richter tuning

This was invented in 1825 or '26 and uses only the notes from one major scale, arranged in such a way that the instrument produces a tonic chord (D on a D harp) when blown and a dominant seventh chord (A7 on a D harp) in the bottom 5 holes when drawn.

This arrangement made the instrument ideal for playing the popular music of the time and, although Richter was from Bohemia and originated the tuning in Vienna, it says much for its versatility that all the manufacturers adopted this tuning in a very short space of time.

Layout of a blues harp in G

BLUES HARPS ARE available in twelve different keys, all of which can be used with this book. The diagram of the notes of the G harmonica below shows that, although the notes are different to those on the D harmonica, they still bear the same **relationship** to each other. This means that any one can be used with this book. If yours is not in D, simply read the numbers or, if you are reading the music, just pretend you have a D instrument. It will just mean that the tune is played higher or lower than the pitch shown by the music.

Note layout on a harmonica in G:

	1	2	3	4	5	6	7	8	9	10	
Blow	G	B	D	G	B	D	G	B	D	G	
Draw	a	d	f♯	a	c	e	f♯	a	c	e	

Notes available on a harmonica in G:

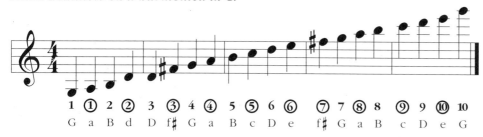

1	①	2	②	3	③	4	④	5	⑤	6	⑥		⑦	7	⑧	8	⑨	9	⑩	10
G	a	B	d	D	f♯	G	a	B	c	D	e		f♯	G	a	B	c	D	e	G

One of the drawbacks of tablature is that while it can tell you **what** notes to play, it cannot tell you **how long** to play them for. It is well worthwhile in the long run for you to gain at least some understanding of musical notation so you can read this information from the music, even if you are reading the actual notes from the tablature.

Double-reeded harmonicas

IF YOU ARE using a double-reed harmonica, it will be either tremolo-tuned or octave-tuned. Both kinds are identifiable by the fact that they have two rows of holes rather than one. Tremolo instruments are straight whereas octave-tuned instruments are curved. If you have an instrument of either of these types, you will possibly need to make some slight adjustments to the tablature and your thinking.

Whereas single-reed harmonicas use the same hole for blow and draw notes, double-reed ones have different holes for each breath direction. They also have two reeds which play simultaneously for each note. Therefore you will have to think of each square group of four holes as being the equivalent of one on the diagram above.

The following tremolo-tuned harmonicas, made by the world famous M. Hohner Ltd. are suitable for use with this book, though you will be very lucky to find one in the key of D, as has already been mentioned.

Echo 2309/32

Echo 2409/40

Echo 2509/48

Echo Double-sided 54/64 (basically, two instruments in different keys built back to back).

Echo Double-sided 55/80

Echo Double-sided 56/96

Echo Double-sided 57/120

Golden Melody 2416/40

Those models with 40 reeds - the 2409, 55 and 2416 correspond most closely in their layout to the diagram - though to get the actual note names you are playing, you will have to do some transposition if your instrument is not in the key of D.

The 2309 and 54 models start higher and finish lower than those already mentioned and, using the four-holes-equals-one principal, are laid out like holes two to nine inclusive in the diagram.

Models 2509 and 56 are similar to the 2309 and 54 but cover a greater range and begin an octave lower than those mentioned. For the purposes of this book treat them as the same thing.

The model 57 covers the widest range of all the Hohner tremolo instruments - use the four-holes-equals-one trick and follow the tablature - your music will sound an octave lower than written, that's all.

Holding the harmonica

THE COMMONEST WAY of holding the harmonica is by lightly gripping the instrument with the crook of the thumb and index finger of your left hand, low notes on the left and the high notes on the right. The little finger of the left hand is then laid along the base of the instrument and the right hand is used to form a cup, or chamber, behind it. This gives access to a range of tonal effects created by opening and closing the chamber.

Really, there are as many ways of doing this as there are harmonica players; the important things are that you feel comfortable, have formed as much of a chamber round the instrument as the size of your hands will allow and that your posture is relaxed so you can breathe freely.

It should be stressed that this is only the basic way of going about it and precisely what you do will vary from instrument to instrument, depending on the size and construction.

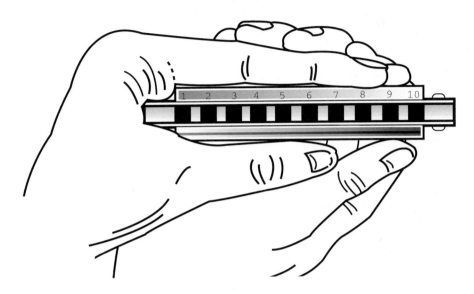

Breathing

NOW, THIS YOU'VE been doing since the midwife turned you upside down and slapped you between the shoulder blades, right? So what's the problem? To get the best from your harmonica you must learn to breathe from the diaphragm. If you're not sure what this means, try the following exercise. Lie on the floor with the soles of your feet on it. Bring your heels towards your buttocks until you feel the small of your back make contact with the floor. Staying relaxed place the backs of your hands on the floor above your head. This will effectively prevent your rib cage from moving and force you to breathe from your diaphragm. Notice how you are now able to completely fill your lungs and how, when you exhale using the same muscle, you are able to 'support' your voice or a note on the harmonica.

First steps in playing

NOW IT'S TIME to combine the holding and breathing techniques. At first, this may feel a bit like patting your head and rubbing your stomach but it won't be long before you find that you need little conscious effort to play the instrument.

To begin, raise the instrument to your lips, fill your lungs and exhale into any hole or holes anywhere on the instrument. **Don't blow** - just breathe through the instrument; imagine that the sound you are producing is like a ping-pong ball held up by a column of air.

Now inhale through your mouth using the same hole or holes. **Don't suck** - this will place undue strain on the reeds and cause them to go out of tune far faster than they normally would. Experiment with different air pressures - you should be able to take the sound from a whisper to a shout without the pitch changing at all. You should particularly concentrate on the lower numbered holes, especially 2 and 3. They are different from all the other holes on the harmonica in that the distance between the blow note and the draw note is greater than a whole tone - it is this fact that enables blues players to get that distinctive 'bluesy' flavour in their playing and is also one that gives new harmonica owners the most trouble, often causing them to believe that there is something wrong with their instrument. 'Taint the case, I'm afraid. What usually causes the sound that comes out from the draw notes in these holes either not to happen at all or to sound like a cat being strangled by a poorly-trained hangman's second under-assistant is the fact that the player is going at it too hard.

As I said, **don't suck** - inhale gently - if you're still having problems, try breathing through your nose at the same time as your mouth, so you can get an idea of the sound you are trying to produce. Don't let this become a habit though; it will be awkward later when you're playing an Irish jig at 500 miles per hour for a team of dancers if you have to try to remember to breathe in through your nose when playing all draw notes in holes 2 and 3. Just use this technique to fix the correct sound for those notes in your head and you'll find that with a little practise you'll have it down pat.

Sounding a single note

I'M SURE YOU'RE keen to get on with playing now, but first something you can work on whilst you study the first couple of pieces; that is, getting a single note to sound. There are two commonly used methods of doing this, each with their own advantages. Good harmonica players outside the field of classical music tend to use both methods almost interchangeably, depending on the effect they are trying to achieve. For the time being use the one that you feel most comfortable with. The first method is known as **puckering** or the 'whistle method'. Here you simply pucker your lips as if to whistle (or drink one of those awful burger bar milk shakes through a straw) and apply your lips to a hole on the harmonica causing the note in it to sound separately, with no interference from neighbouring notes. It may take a little time to master this but bear in mind the fact that it is vital to get a good seal around the mouthpiece of the instrument and that the further you can get the mouthpiece into your mouth - whilst still getting a single note - the better the seal is likely to be.

To separate single notes, use the technique known as **tongueing -** move the tip of your tongue as if to say 'ta' as you play each note. If you are using the next method, tongue-blocking, use 'ka'.

Mouth position for 'puckering'

The second method, known as **tongue-blocking,** involves covering three or four holes with your mouth and blocking the holes you don't want to sound with the tip of your relaxed tongue, so that only the note on the right (or left) of the group is played. One advantage of this in playing folk music is that by lifting the tongue on and off the mouthpiece rhythmically, some great self-accompaniment effects can be achieved. It is important to note that when using this technique the harmonica is blown from the side of the mouth rather than the centre. The Northumbrian player Willie Atkinson is delightfully adept at this technique. *The Trip to Cullenstown* (Claddagh Records 4CC55) is a landmark recording of three County Wexford harmonicists, John, Phil and Pip Murphy. They too excel with this earthy-sounding 'vamping' accompaniment style. The recordings of Scottish player Arthur Middleton are also well worth tracking down, listening to and studying.

Mouth position for 'tongue-blocking'

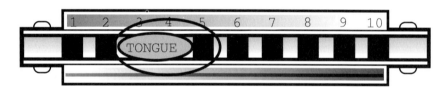

Further information

FOR BASIC MUSIC theory, see page 2.

If you are having trouble with the material in this book, call the harmonica hotline on 01604 832726, where an experienced player will be able to help. More about the diatonic harmonica, including bending notes and the physics of how bending works can be found in **The Harp Handbook** by Steve Baker.

More information about basic bending techniques can be found in **Bending the Blues** by David Harp.

Right, let's play some music...

Skip to My Lou

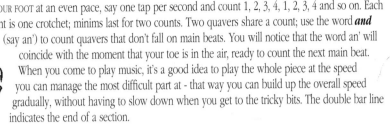

TAP YOUR FOOT at an even pace, say one tap per second and count 1, 2, 3, 4, 1, 2, 3, 4 and so on. Each count is one crotchet; minims last for two counts. Two quavers share a count; use the word **and** (say an') to count quavers that don't fall on main beats. You will notice that the word an' will coincide with the moment that your toe is in the air, ready to count the next main beat. When you come to play music, it's a good idea to play the whole piece at the speed you can manage the most difficult part at - that way you can build up the overall speed gradually, without having to slow down when you get to the tricky bits. The double bar line indicates the end of a section.

Counting ⁴⁄₄ time

1   2   3   4   1 (2) 3 an' 4 an'   1 (2) (3) 4   1 (2) an' 3   4

If you're having trouble picking out single notes, don't worry - keep working at it. Bear in mind that these early tunes have been carefully selected so that they will sound good even if you're playing more than one note at a time. The important thing is to make sure that the notes shown in the music are the furthest right in the group of holes you are playing - the lower notes will then provide an 'easy on the ear' accompaniment. Use the tongueing technique to produce distinct notes and remember to **br-ea-th-e** through the harmonica, not at it. Bear in mind also that your effective concentration span is limited - do something else for a while if you're having real trouble - your subconscious will still be beavering away at whatever the problem is!

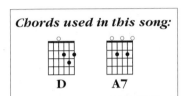

Chords used in this song:

D   A7

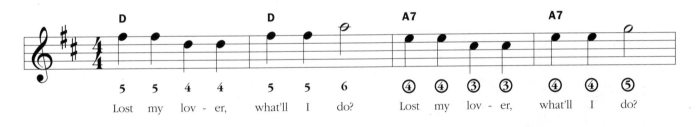

5   5   4   4   5   5   6   ④   ④   ③   ③   ④   ④   ⑤

Lost   my   lov - er,   what'll   I   do?   Lost   my   lov - er,   what'll   I   do?

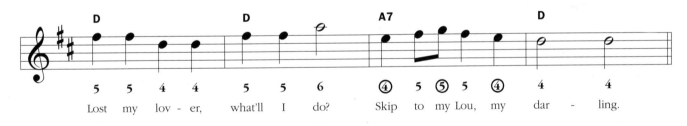

5   5   4   4   5   5   6   ④   5   ⑤   5   ④   4   4

Lost   my   lov - er,   what'll   I   do?   Skip   to   my   Lou,   my   dar - ling.

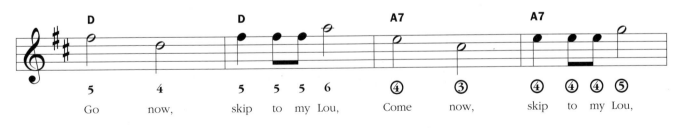

5   4   5   5   5   6   ④   ③   ④   ④   ④   ⑤

Go   now,   skip   to   my   Lou,   Come   now,   skip   to   my   Lou,

5   4   5   5   6   ④   5   ⑤   5   ④   4   4

Run   now,   skip   to   my   Lou,   Skip   to   my   Lou,   my   dar - ling.

7

Coulter's Candy

AS THIS IS such a short tune, you might want to play it through a couple of times - try playing single notes only the first time through and pairs of notes on the second time for variety and to maintain the listener's interest.

The curved line above the sixth bar in this song is an indication of how to sing the words underneath. Ignore such slurs, as they're known, for now. They'll be tackled later in the book and are shown for consistency.

Chords used in this song:

D   G   Em   A7

D			G	D	D		Em	A7
4	5	6	6	⑥ 6 ⑤ ⑥ 6	4	5	6 6	⑤ 5	④

Al - lee, bal - lee, al - lee bal - lee bee, Sitt - ing on your mam - my's knee,

D			G	D	D		A7	D
4	5	6	6	⑥ 6 ⑤ ⑥ 6	5 4	5	6 5	④	4

Greet - ing for a - nith - er baw - bee, Tae buy mair Coul - ter's can - dy

Fare Thee Well, Enniskillen

Lead-in bar

THE SUM OF the notes in bars of music is always equal to the amount indicated by the time signature. Bars of ²⁄₄ time contain 'two crotchets worth' of notes; bars of ³⁄₄ time contain 'three crotchets worth', and so on.

Most songs and tunes start just before the main beat occurs, so there is a short 'lead-in' bar at the beginning. This short bar becomes part of the last bar on repeating. The notes missing from the last bar are found in the 'lead-in' bar.

Chords used in this song:

D   Em   A7   Bm   F♯m

You may hear the 'lead-in' bar called other things like the 'pick-up' or (mainly by classical musicians) an 'anacrusis'. Single notes are important in this tune because the note 7 draw will sound very rough if you play 6 draw at the same time - try it and see!

```
       D              Em            A7              D
   6  5    4   ④   5   ⑤  ④  6  ⑤   ④    4   ③    4        6
 Fare thee  well,  Enn-is-kill-en  fare thee  well  for  a   while;   And
```

```
  Bm           F♯m          Em              A7
  7   ⑥   7   ⑦  6  ⑥  ⑤   ④   5   ⑤    6    ⑥   ⑦
 all 'round the  bor —— ders of  Er-in's green isle,  And_____
```

```
  Bm           F♯m          Em              A7
  7  7  ⑥  7   ⑦  6  ⑥  ⑤   ④   5   ⑤    6    ⑤   ④
 when the war is  o-ver, we'll re-turn  in  full bloom,  And we'll
```

```
  D              Em            A7              D
  4   ④   5   ⑤  ④  6  ⑤   ④    4   ③    4
 all  wel-come  home the Enn-is-kill-en  drag-oons.
```

Little Brown Jug

Guitar accompaniment

USUALLY, MELODIES ARE not played or sung solo, they have some kind of accompaniment. Why not find a friend who plays guitar or keyboards or even a chord harmonica to accompany your tunes? You will find that your music becomes much more fun and the experience of playing with others can be very rewarding. To facilitate this, chord names have been included above the stave. Very basic versions of the guitar chord shapes these represent are shown in a separate box on each page. Any reasonable book of chord shapes will give you some challenging alternatives.

Chords used in this song:
D G A

Counting ²⁄₄ time

1 (an') 2 (an') 1(an)(2)(an') 1 an' 2 er an' er 1 (an') (2) an' 1 an' er 2 (an') er

My wife and I liv'd all a-lone in a wee log hut we call'd our own,

She lov'd gin and I lov'd rum and I tell you we had lots of fun!

Ha ha ha, you and me, Lit-tle brown jug I do love thee,

Ha ha ha, you and me, Lit-tle brown jug don't I love thee?

My Bonny Lies Over the Ocean

Counting ¾ time

THIS TUNE IS in ¾ time, like a waltz. Count 1, 2, 3, 1, 2, 3 etc. Use 'an' to count the quavers. It also introduces the tie. A tie joins two (or more) notes of the same pitch together, indicating a single, sustained note with a time value equal to the combined value of the tied notes.

Another new item is the *8va* above the music. This means that all the notes under the dotted lines are to be played an octave higher than written. This has been taken into account in preparing the tablature but at least you know what it means now. This usually only applies to a small section of a tune; however, in the case of this book a number of tunes have to be raised by one octave in their entirety, therefore, to make the music less cluttered the symbol *8va* will only appear at the beginning of a tune in the rest of this book, meaning raise the whole tune by an octave.

Chords used in this song:
D G E7 A7

Beginners Harmonica

The Old Woman from Wexford

Counting ⁶⁄₈ time

Hump - ty Dump - ty   sat   on a   wall

THIS TUNE INTRODUCES a new time signature, ⁶⁄₈. It is different to ³⁄₄ in that it has two strong beats in every bar. It is best understood by bearing in mind the rhythm of the words to 'Humpty Dumpty'.

In the first complete bar of the tune, you will see several repeated notes of the same pitch. If you are taking the tune at a fair speed, you may find it appropriate to make use of a technique called **double-tongueing**. This does not mean that you have to acquire an extra tongue from somewhere but simply that instead of using the tip of your tongue to make a 'ta' sound for each note, you alternate the 'ta' with 'ka'. Another idea is to use 'diddley' for each group of three notes.

Experiment with these ideas and see which works best for you.

Chords used in this song:

D   A7   G

Well, there was an old wo-man from Wex - ford, in Wex-ford town did dwell;___ She

lov'd her hus - band dear - ly, lov'd a - noth - er man twice as well, With me

whack fol didd - le um dare um, with me whack fol dur um day.

British Grenadiers

Slurring

FOR THIS TUNE, try using a technique called **slurring**. This means that instead of playing each note as a distinct and separate entity, you should try to play as smoothly as possible, within the confines of changes of breath direction, moving the instrument etc. Where you find a series of notes that are in adjacent holes and are all either blown or drawn, try simply moving the harmonica across your mouth while maintaining a steady stream of air. The notes will still be separated from one another by the lateral movement of the instrument, but the music should sound smoother. Try also to 'even things out', so that you cannot hear the difference between blow and draw notes. You may find it useful to work with a tape recorder for this exercise.

Chords used in this song:

D   A   D7   G   E7

Some talk of Al - ex - an - der and___ some of Her - cu - les; Of

Hec - tor and Ly - san - da and___ such great names___ as___ these. But of

all the world's great he___roes, there's none that can___ com - pare___ with the

tow row,___ row row,___ tow row___ row of the Brit - ish Gren - a - diers!

The Wild Colonial Boy

Grace notes

IN THIS TUNE, try another method of separating notes of the same pitch - by the use of grace notes. A grace note is a quick note which steals its time from the note it precedes. Fiddle and whistle players are able to use the note above or below the 'target note'. The layout of the harmonica militates against this approach but it is just as valid to use the note with the same breath direction in an adjacent hole. Try using grace notes both higher and lower in pitch than the target note and see which you prefer.

Chords used in this song: D G Em A

6 4 5 6 6 ⑥ ⑤ ④ 4 ③ 3 5 ④ 4 5 ⑤
There was a wild col - o - nial boy, Jack Dugg - an was his name._____ He was

6 7 7 6 ⑦ ⑥ ④ 5 5 ⑤ 6 ⑦ ⑥ 6 5
born and rais'd in I - re - land, in a place called Cas - tle - maine,_____ He

6 7 7 6 ⑦ ⑥ ④ 5 ⑤ 6 ⑦ ⑥ 6 5
was his fa - ther's on - ly son, his mo - ther's pride and joy;_____ A

4 5 6 6 ⑥ ⑤ ④ 4 ③ 3 5 ④ 4
cred - it to old Ire - land was the wild col - o - nial boy._____

Lizzie Lindsay

Breathing and phrasing

ONE OF THE advantages harmonica players have over players of other wind instruments is the fact that the harmonica contains both blow and draw notes, which makes sustained breathing through a musical phrase less of a problem than it might be for, say, a flautist. Even so you may encounter passages containing either mostly blow or mostly draw notes, which will leave your lungs either too empty or too full. There are two ways of dealing with this.

If you are at the end of a musical phrase (generally only two or four bars in length), you can steal time from the last note to deflate or inflate your lungs, as appropriate.

If you get into trouble during a phrase, look out for the next blow note, if your lungs are full, and breathe out through your nose (silently, please!) at the same time as you play the note. Similarly, if your lungs are getting empty, look out for the next draw note and breathe in through your nose as you play it, to replenish your air supply. It may take a little practise before you quite get the hang of this but soon it will become second nature. Remember that the most important thing is that your music should make sense and that it is made up of phrases and 'sentences', just like a spoken language.

Chords used in this song:

D   Bm   D7   G   A

15

Beginners Harmonica

John Barleycorn

Rests

IN MUSIC, PERIODS of silence are called *rests.* Each note value has an equivalent rest. A period of silence one crotchet in duration is shown thus: 𝄽 and a period of silence shown as the symbol 𝄾 is equivalent in duration to one quaver.

Chords used in this song:

D   A   G   A7

Annie Laurie

Long distance jumping

WATCH OUT IN this tune for the several occasions where the note following the one you are playing is **not** in an adjacent hole. Of course, one way of getting from say blow 4 to blow 7 is to keep blowing, move the harmonica playing blow 5 and blow 6 as grace notes and arrive at blow 7 to the rousing plaudits of the crowd - or not, as the case may be. Ornamentation of this sort should not, in any event, be overdone and the musical circumstances will not always be right.

Practise making **all** the jumps from one hole to another, playing them as distinct and separate notes; once you have learned all the distances between non-adjacent holes, you will begin to feel much more confident and secure about your playing.

Beginners Harmonica

Sally Gardens

Repeated parts

THIS TUNE INTRODUCES repeats. The double bar line *preceded* by two dots means go back to the last double bar line *succeeded* by two dots or the beginning and play the section again. The first time you play a section, play the bar marked 1 and on the second time, the bar marked 2.

This tune is a reel, one of the most popular forms of dance tune among musicians. Remember that this is music to be *danced to* while you are playing. This tune is usually played in G; this presents no problem at all, just put your D harmonica in your pocket and play the tune on your G exactly as you have learned it, when joining in with other musicians.

Chords used in this tune:

D   Em   A   A7   E7

Cockles and Mussels

Chords used in this song:

D Bm7 Em7 A7 E7

More repeats

THIS TUNE INTRODUCES another way of showing a repeat. The **D.C.** at the end of the last bar is an abbreviation of the Italian **Da Capo,** which means, in music, *go back to the beginning and play the whole lot again.*

19

Beginners Harmonica

My Love is Like a Red, Red Rose

Achieving a better tone

THIS LOVELY BALLAD gives you the opportunity to play with the sweetest and fullest tone you can muster. Try to keep your throat open all the time, almost as if you were yawning. Don't allow your tongue to get too far back in your mouth.

One key to a good tone on the harmonica is an awareness that the player's body is a main resonator for the sound.

Chords used in this song:

D   A   G   Em   A7

Scarborough Fair

Minor keys

ALL THE TUNES so far have been in the key of D major, denoted by the two sharps in the key signature. As well as major keys there are also minor keys, which have a more plaintive quality. This one is in E minor and you will be playing in the *third position* (see page 22). Many traditional tunes are in minor keys.

Chords used in this song:

Em   B7   G   A   C   D

Beginners Harmonica

The Keel Row

A new rhythm

THE DOTTED QUAVER/SEMIQUAVER pairs sound like **dah-di.** Use double-tongueing in bars 1, 3 and 5.

Chords used in this tune:

D   A7   G

Transposing

CHANGING MUSIC FROM one key to another is known as **transposing.** It is possible to change key or **transpose** on the harmonica simply by swapping instruments. Over the years, though, a system has evolved among harmonica players that refers to the ways in which different keys can be played on one instrument as **positions;** most of the music in this book is played in what is known as the **first position.** The key of the music played in this position will be the key marked on the harmonica. The other positions are based on what is known as the **circle of fifths.** Most players (even professionals) stick to first, second and third positions most of the time. Second position is particularly popular in blues, country and rock music and can present problems to the player of traditional music. Really, the positions are a shorthand way of describing where the **home, root** or **key** note of a piece of music is to be found. Thus, in first position, the home note is always found in holes 1, 4, 7 and 10 blow, irrespective of the key of the harmonica. In second position it is in 2 draw and 3, 6 and 9 blow. In third position, it is in holes 1, 4 and 8 draw.

This little diagram will help you to work out what keys are available to you in these positions on harmonicas in all keys.

Transfer the cursor to a piece of thin card and line the arrow up with D. You will see that first position on a D harmonica gives you, yes, the key of D. Second position gives A and third gives E minor. Now move the cursor to G. Here, first position is G, second is D and third is now A minor. Moving the cursor to A shows first position to be A, second E and third B minor. So, with three harmonicas, you can cover the most popular keys in folk music, both on the printed page and in 'live' situations.

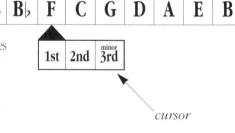

F♯	D♭	A♭	E♭	B♭	F	C	G	D	A	E	B

1st 2nd minor 3rd

cursor

If we come at this from a slightly different angle, say, you are asked to sit in with a group and they want to play a tune in the key of F, then by lining up the three positions on the cursor with F, you find that you could play either an F harmonica in first position, a B flat harmonica in second position or, if the tune is minor, an E♭ harmonica in third position.

Transposing written music

TO TRANSPOSE A piece of music to another key, first change the key signature, then all occurrences of the root note; then, raise or lower all the other notes by the same number of lines and spaces. The circle of fifths comes in handy here, too.

Say you are transposing a piece from D into G. You take away 1 sharp from the key signature, change all the Ds to Gs and then, because G is one to the left of D in the diagrams, use the diagram to help you move all the other notes 'one to the left' as well.

The Wearin' o' the Green

Beginners Harmonica

The Skye Boat Song

Different endings

THIS TUNE BRINGS in another way in which repeats are used. Play all the way down to the repeat sign and there you will see the words **D.C. al fine**, which means *go back to the beginning and play until you reach the word 'Fine'*. The end of bar eight is the **Fine** in this case. Fine - pronounced *feenay* - means end. All this adds up to playing the whole thing once, then the first eight bars again.

The dotted quaver/semiquaver/quaver groups may be thought of as sounding like **DAH-di-dee.** Take the time to familiarise yourself with this rhythm, as it crops up time and again in folk music. Take care not to let it sound like a waltz.

Chords used in this song:

D   Bm   A   G   A7   Em

6 ⑥ 6 7 7 7 ⑧ 8 ⑧ 9 8 ⑧ 8 ⑥ ⑥ 6
Speed, bon-nie boat like a bird on the wing, on-wards the sail-ors cry,_____

6 ⑥ 6 7 7 ⑧ 8 ⑧ 9 8 ⑧ 8 ⑥ ⑥ 6
Car-ry the lad that's born to be king, o-ver the sea to Skye;_____

8 7 8 8 ⑧ ⑥ ⑧ ⑧ 7 ⑥ 7 7 7 ⑥
Loud the winds howl, loud the waves roar, thun-der-claps rend the air,_____

8 7 8 8 ⑧ ⑥ ⑧ ⑧ 7 ⑥ 7 7 7 ⑥ 6
Baf-fled our foes stand by the shore, fol-low they will not dare, Oh

New York Girls

Revision

THE NEXT PIECES are intended as revision - they do not introduce any new concepts but should be thoroughly mastered before you proceed further.

Chords used in this song:

D G A7

D	G	A7	D

6 5 6 6 5 ⑤ ⑥ 7 ⑦ 6 ⑤ 6 5 6

As I walk'd down the Broad-way___ one eve-ning in Ju-ly, I

D	G	A7	D

7 7 7 6 ⑦ ⑥ ⑥ ⑥ 6 6 ⑤ ④ 4 ④ 5 ⑤

met a maid who ask'd me trade, "A sail-or John," say I,___ And a-

D	G	A7	D

6 5 ⑤ ⑥ 6 ⑤ 5 4

way you San-tee,___ my dear An-nie;___

D	G	A7	D

7 6 ⑦ ⑥ ⑥ 6 6 ⑤ ③ ④ 4

All you New York girls, can't ye dance the pol-ka?___

Beginners Harmonica

The Campañero

Henry the Poacher

Chords used in this song: D G A7

Come all you wild and wick-ed youths wher-ev-er you may___ be, I pray you give at-ten-tion and lis-ten un-to me, The fate of us poor trans-ports as you shall un-der-stand, The hard-ships that we un-der-go up-on Van Die-man's Land;___ Young men all now be-ware lest you be drawn in-to a snare.

Beginners Harmonica

Phil the Fluter's Ball

THIS WELL-KNOWN MELODY is an ideal show-case for your harmonica skills. Decorate it in accordance with your feelings and remember that music should be fun, not boring hard work.

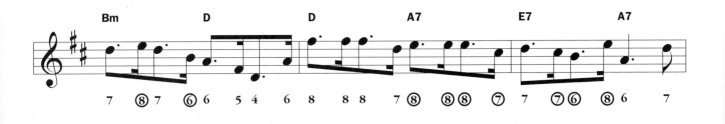

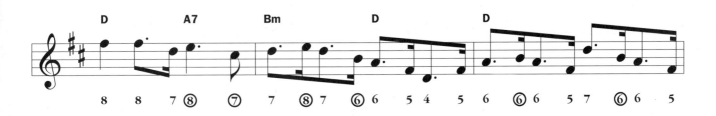

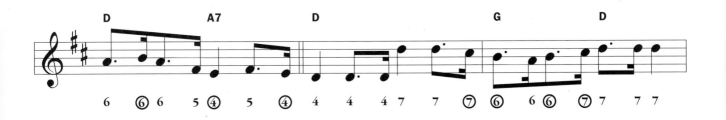

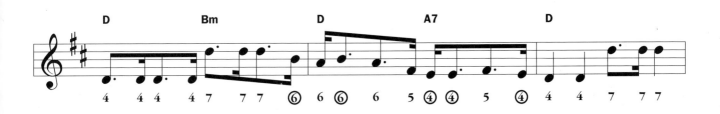

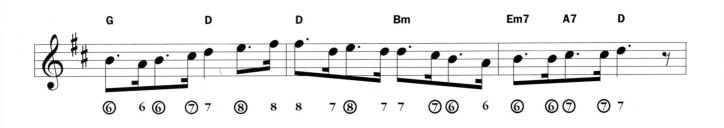

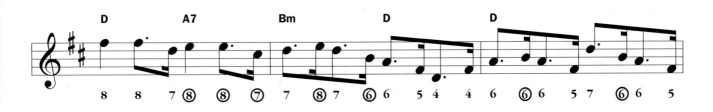

Beginners Harmonica

Doctor O'Neill

THIS IS AN Irish jig which lies, as you will discover, quite comfortably on the harmonica. Many other Irish tunes, more usually associated with the fiddle, have this characteristic in common. Remember that this is dance music so play it in a lively rhythmic manner. To hear this type of music played brilliantly on the harmonica listen to the album *New Irish Harmonica* (*Punch Music PM002*) by Brendan Power.

Chords used in this tune:

D   Em   G   A7   Bm   F♯m   A

31

Carrickfergus